THE
DIRECTORY
FOR HEADSHOT PHOTOGRAPHY

Editor: Cameron Stewart

Design: Cameron Stewart

Production: Bert Lee
Eric Dolgins
Daniel Wood

Coordination: Eric Dolgins

Sales: Cameron Stewart

Publisher: Cameron Stewart Inc.

Artwork: Michael Eade

Printing: Bowne de Montréal

Reproductions

THE DIRECTORY FOR HEADSHOT PHOTOGRAPHY '99-'00

The performing arts as in all other industries, includes the need for good information as a precursor to success. The Directory connects talent with that success. Through a "pictures tell the story design", The Directory has become a proven and vital aid in pursuing and achieving success in the performing arts industry.

Reproductions is proud to contribute to your industry and thankful for the support from the artists The Directory serves.

Table Of Contents

PHOTOGRAPHERS

TRADE

PHOTOGRAPHERS

CHIA MESSINA

212.929.0917

15 WEST 24 STREET NEW YORK NEW YORK 10010

CHIA MESSINA

212.929.0917

15 WEST 24 STREET NEW YORK NEW YORK 10010

Steve
Kahn
1.212.334.2139

"Only a select few headshots remain on a Casting Director's desk...

ROBERT KIM PHOTOGRAPHY

...make sure that yours is one of them."

11

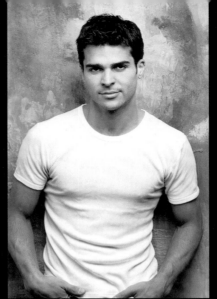

James J. Kriegsmann Jr.

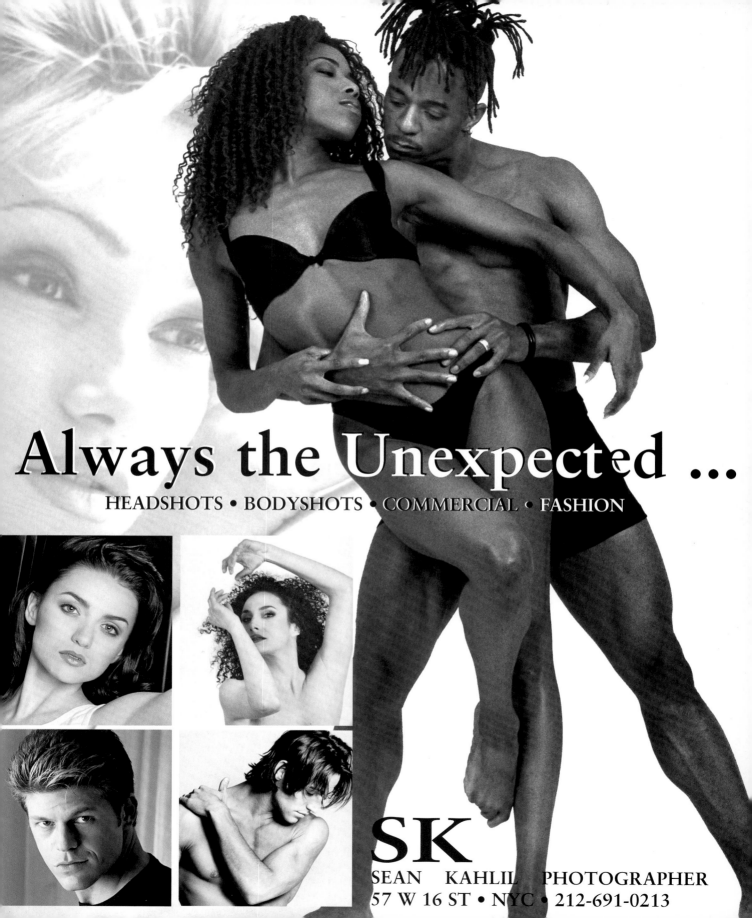

Ariel Jones

212.513.1090

Ariel Jones

212.513.1090

15

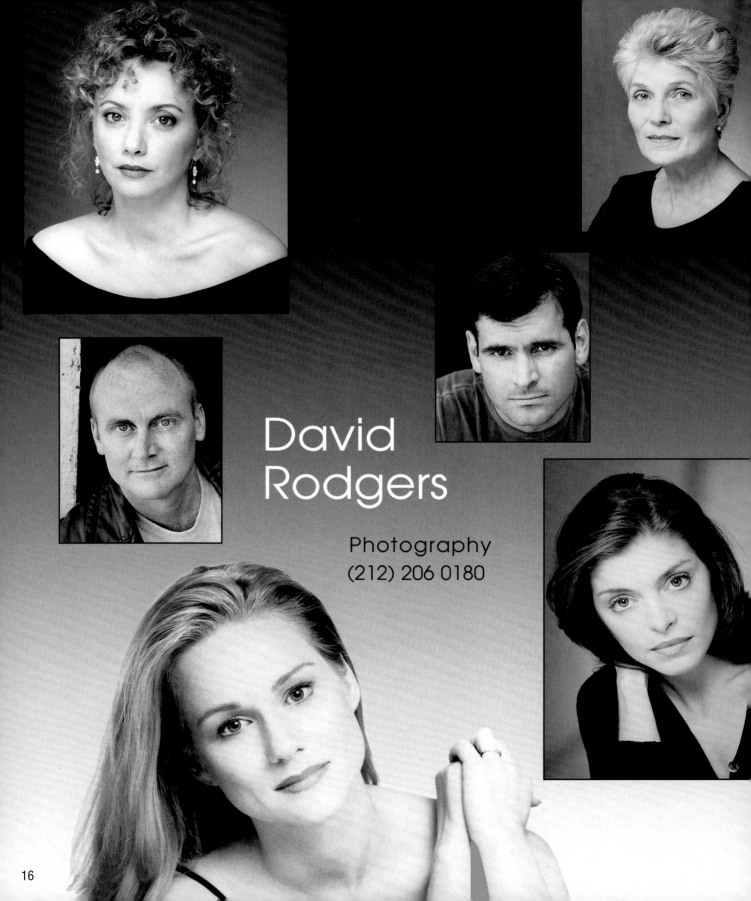

David
Rodgers

Photography
(212) 206 0180

16

HOEBERMANN STUDIO

281 Sixth Avenue, New York, N.Y. 10014 212 807-8014

HOEBERMANN STUDIO

281 Sixth Avenue, New York, N.Y. 10014 212 807-8014

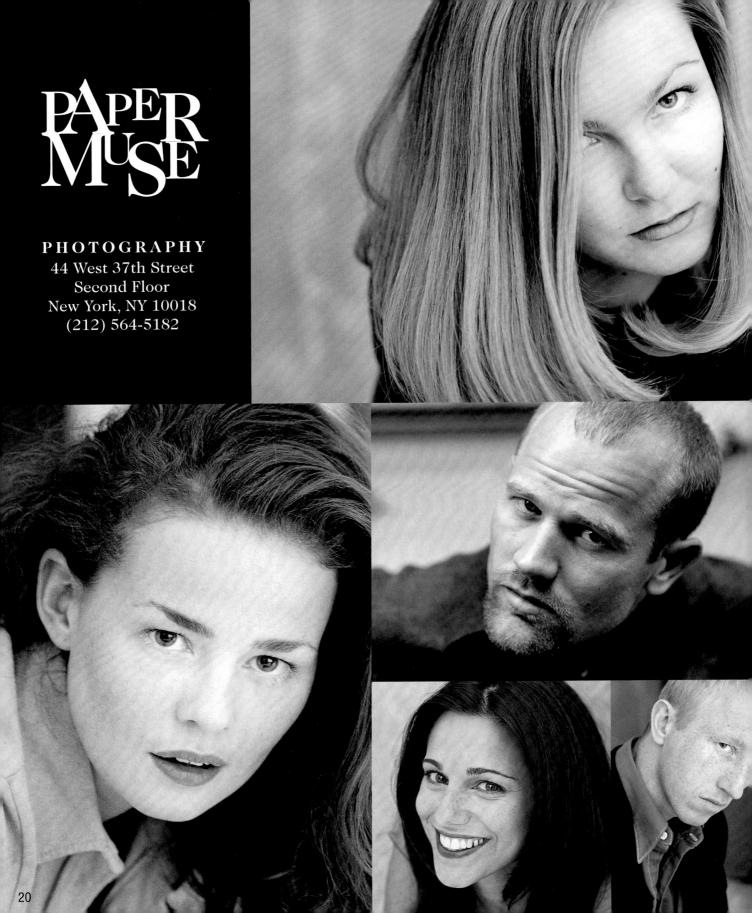

PAPER MUSE

PHOTOGRAPHY
44 West 37th Street
Second Floor
New York, NY 10018
(212) 564-5182

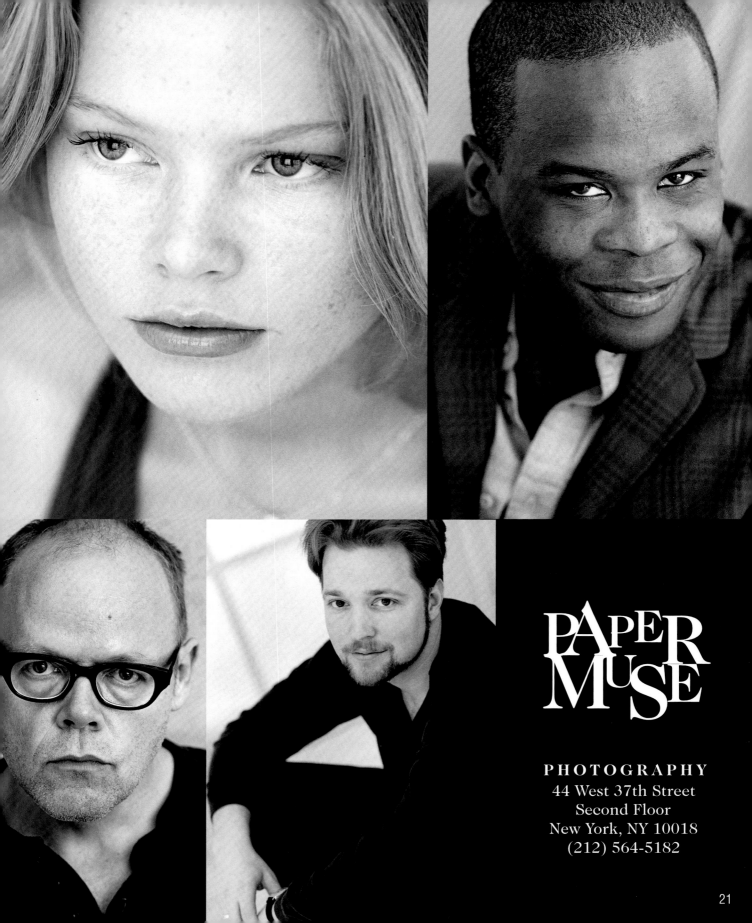

21

THADDEUS WATKINS
212 736 0776

252 West 37th Street, 18th Floor   New York City   10018

THADDEUS WATKINS
2 1 2   7 3 6   0 7 7 6

252 West 37th Street, 18th Floor   New York City   10018

Barbara Vaughn

BARBARA VAUGHN

BARBARA VAUGHN

Julie Brimberg

P H O T O G R A P H Y
212 ▪ 425 ▪ 6759

DEBORAH LOPEZ
STUDIO
212 594 8273

DEBORAH LOPEZ

STUDIO

212 594 8273

31

PETER SWEYER PHOTOGRAPHY
CHELSEA STUDIO CELL 917.488.7946

CALCATERRA2126044874

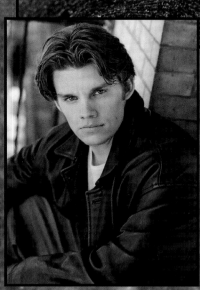

CROSS New York
photography

DAVE CROSS PHOTOGRAPHY

119 West 23rd Street Suite 409 New York NY 10011
Tel (212) 255 8212 Fax (212) 924 7439

CROSBY PHOTOGRAPHY
212-877-1935

CROSBY PHOTOGRAPHY

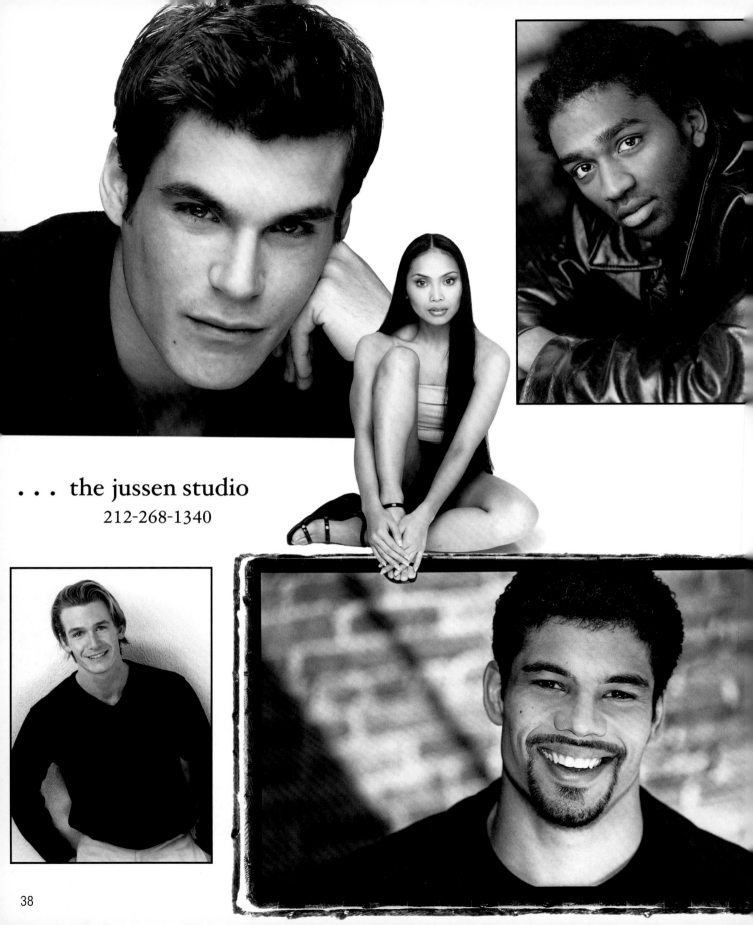

... the jussen studio
212-268-1340

... the jussen studio

212-268-1340

Manning Gurney
PHOTOGRAPHY

25 WEST 38TH STREET NEW YORK, N.Y. 10018 (212) 391-0965

Manning Gurney
PHOTOGRAPHY

25 WEST 38TH STREET NEW YORK, N.Y. 10018 (212) 391-0965

Photography...

joe
henson
212.463.0575

joe
henson

Photography
236 West 27th St. Suite 10RW
New York, NY 10001
212.463.0575
212.463.0608 Fax

Portraiture.

JOE GAFFNEY

PHOTOGRAPHER
TEL. (212) 787-0691
FAX (212) 787-0929

JOE GAFFNEY

PHOTOGRAPHER
TEL. (212) 787-0691
FAX (212) 787-0929

TESS STEINKOLK

PHOTOGRAPHER

BROWN DOG PRODUCTIONS, INC.

180 Varick Street, 12th Floor, New York, NY 10014

Tel/Fax 212 627 1366

ILFORD
BLACK & WHITE
PRODUCTS

212-645-9205

© Robert Blosser 1999

PUTTING BLACK & WHITE TO WORK FOR YOU.

ILFORD PHOTO, West 70 Century Road, Paramus, NJ 07653

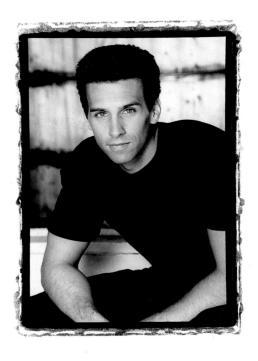

ROBERT VANCE BLOSSER
P H O T O G R A P H Y
212.645.9205

ROBERT VANCE BLOSSER
P H O T O G R A P H Y
212.645.9205

Debra Greenfield

p h o t o g r a p h y

212 • 533 • 0744
142 E. 16th Street NYC
dgreenfield@juno.com

Debra Greenfield
p h o t o g r a p h y

212•533•0744
142 E. 16th Street NYC
dgreenfield@juno.com

53

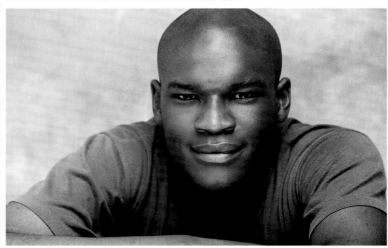

KAROL DUCLOS
PHOTOGRAPHY
212-447-1993
karolduclos.com

KAROL DUCLOS
PHOTOGRAPHY
212-447-1993
karolduclos.com

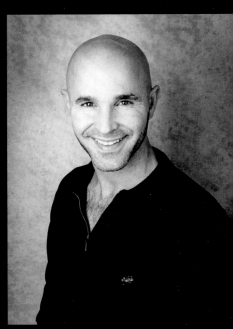

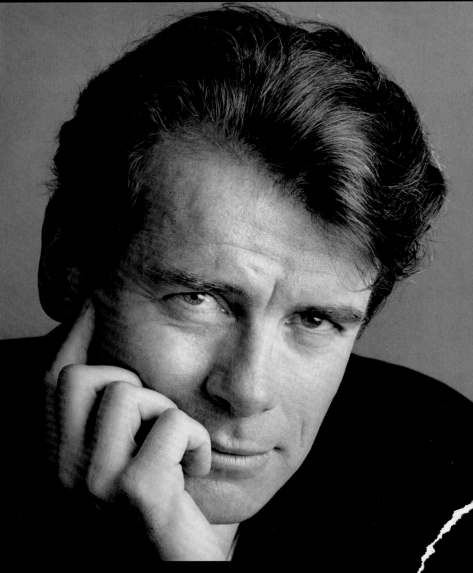

beth kelly
photography

265 west 30th street
new york city 10001
212 868-1604

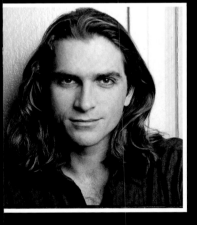

KGM
STUDIOS

212 • 543 • 3782

DAVIDMORGAN
N E W Y O R K

Call 212 989 3880 for complete information 24 hours a day

DAVIDMORGAN
N E W Y O R K

Call 212 989 3880 for complete information 24 hours a day

Lindholm ~ Studio
NYC

JEFF GEORGE PHOTOGRAPHIC

(212) 354-4933
24 W. 39th St. 3rd Floor, NYC 10018

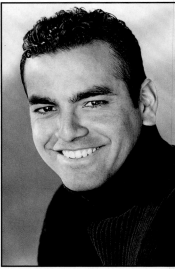

Denise Winters

•HEADSHOTS•

N.Y. 212•355•5223
www.denisewinters.com

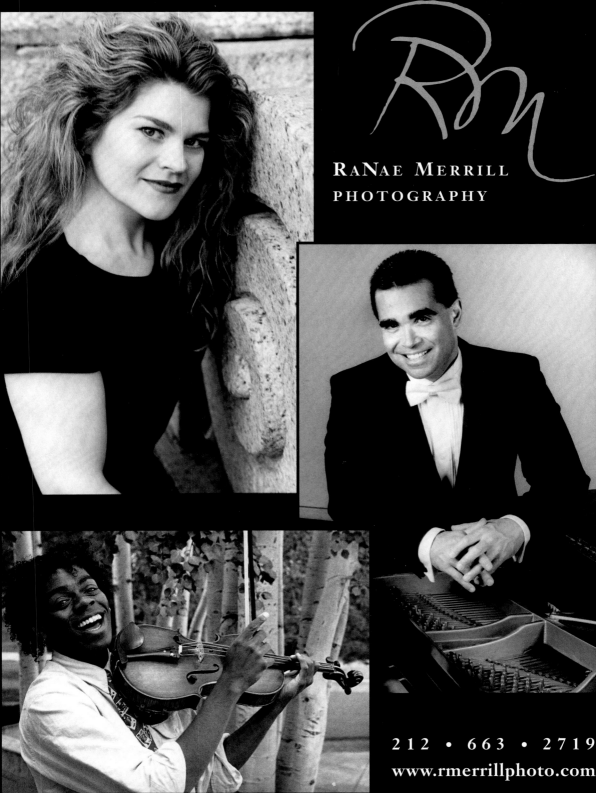

cohen

arthur cohen photography
212 691 5244

cohen

212 691 5244

TIMOTHY LAMPSON
(212) 580-4438

http://hometown.aol.com/TLampson/photos.html

C. Day
Photography
(212) 873-5945

The shots that work for you!

Thomson Photos
(212) 645-5540

Thomson Photos
(212) 645-5540

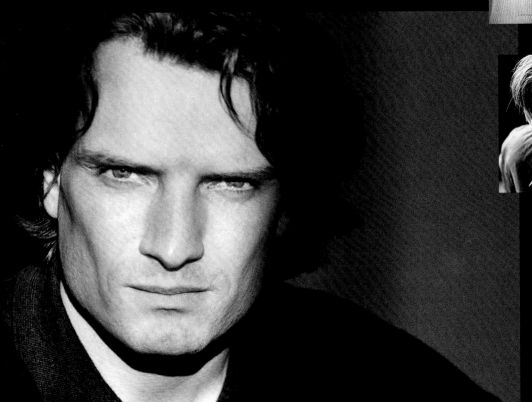

SPELIOTIS photography

212 966-0500

www.yourtype.com/speliotis/

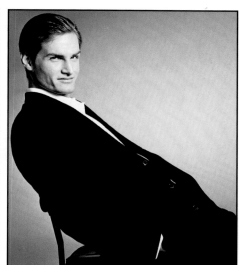

SPELIOTIS photography

212 966-0500

www.yourtype.com/speliotis/

JOHN
FIRMAN
212.794.2794

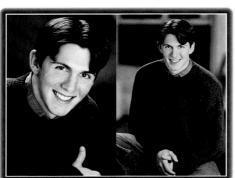

Simply...

bill morris studio

soho . NYC . 212.274.1177

Nick Granito

212.684.1056
nickgranito.com

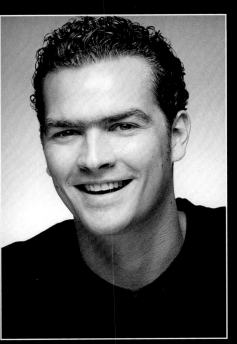

NICK GRANITO

212.684.1056
nickgranito.com

TIM SCHULTHEIS PHOTOGRAPHY
212.721.0829

TIM SCHULTHEIS PHOTOGRAPHY
212.721.0829

A   N   D   R   E   W
ROSENTHAL
PHOTOGRAPHY

448 W.37TH STREET #6F N.Y.C. N.Y. 10018
TEL. 212 760-0266 FAX. 212 967-8051

A N D R E W
R O S E N T H A L
P H O T O G R A P H Y
4 4 8   W . 3 7 T H   S T R E E T   # 6 F   N . Y . C .   N . Y .   1 0 0 1 8
T E L .   2 1 2   7 6 0 - 0 2 6 6   F A X .   2 1 2   9 6 7 - 8 0 5 1

BLANCHE MACKEY

photographer for the performing arts

212.633.6869

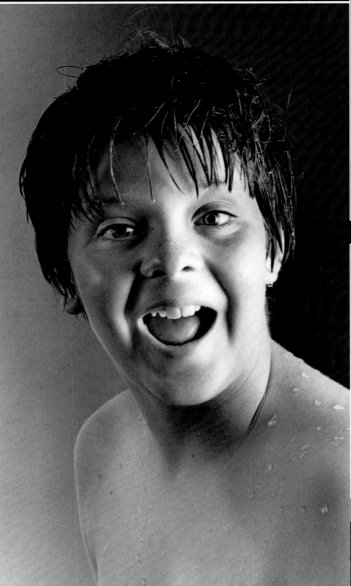

Charles D. Robison

Photography

PHONE: 212.777.4894
FAX: 212.777.7033

Babaldi
Photography

212.253.8795

Headshots

Portraits

Portfolios

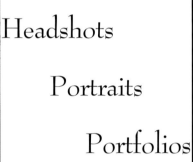

Milano
New York
Roma

Babaldi
Photography

212.253.8795

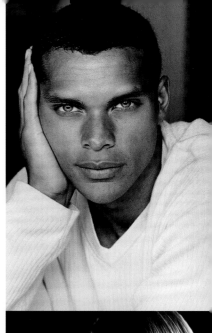

Light Is
Beautiful

ROBERT MANNIS PHOTOGRAPHY

212.591.1285

STEPHANIE BADINI PHOTOGRAPHY

373 BROADWAY F2. NEW YORK. NEW YORK 10013. TELEPHONE 212.966.9524

Richard Blinkoff photography

212-620-7883
147 West 15th Street
NYC 10011

Evan Cohen

PHOTOGRAPHY

212 242-0350

socrates
diamant
photography
(212) 581-5859
asocstudio@aol.com

socrates
diamant
photography
(212) 581-5859
asocstudio@aol.com

KEN WEINGART
PHOTOGRAPHY
212·979·8978

KEN WEINGART
PHOTOGRAPHY
212·979·8978

MARIO VAN PEEBLES, FRANK WHALEY, JOHN SINGLETON, ROBERT SEAN LEONARD, STUART JENKINS, MICHAEL DI BIENVILLE, DARRYL CAREY, MATTHEW ELLISON, CHAZZ PALMINTERI.

Barry Burns

PHOTOGRAPHER

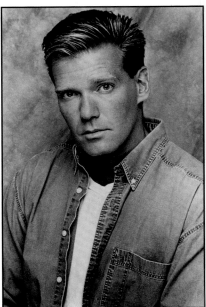

Photographers Note

Every actor has unique characteristics that have to be captured during the photo session. I help my clients relax and express themselves to create spontaneous moments, expressions and gestures that show your distinct, dynamic and colorful personality.

My headshots reveal more than superficial appearance. I actually capture the life that is inside each of my subjects. I seek the unusual, the image that projects energy and spirit.

311 W 43 St.   212 . 713 . 0100
New York, NY 10036

IN THE HEART OF THE THEATER DISTRICT

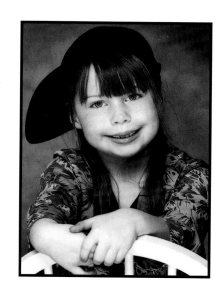

RAY BLOCK STUDIO
2 1 2 · 9 6 7 · 9 4 7 0
Hair and Make-up: Jean Block

Mark Rubin
Photography

55 Bethune St New York NY 10014   *212•929•0293*   www.markrubinphotography.com

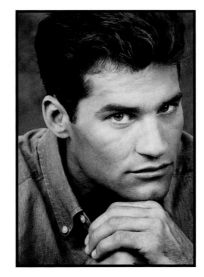

V. MAX
PHOTOGRAPHY
212·886·3720

SCOTT WYNN
PHOTOGRAPHY

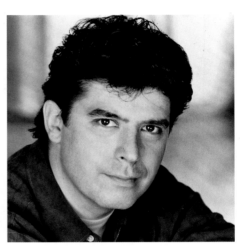

212·874·1449
3 rolls, 108 shots $325

ARIES

PHOTOGRAPHY

2 I 2 . 3 5 8 . 8 6 7 I

Larry Kosson
PO Box 43158
Upper Montclair NJ 07043
973•746•6943   212•255•9893
info@dejaviewphotography.com

DEJA VIEW

p h o t o g r a p h y

©Julie Brimberg

Kodak Professional

Take Pictures. Further.™

The Timeless Vitality
of Agfa Black & White

Capture every subtle nuance with fine grain Agfapan 25.
Agfa film is available at Reproductions.

**Agfa professional black and white
films and papers**

 AgfaCorp., 100 Challanger Road, Ridgfield Park, NJ 07660 ©1999   Agfa is a registered trademark of Agfa-Gevaert, Leverkusen/Antwerp

INDEX OF PHOTOGRAPHERS

Jinsey Dauk
666 Greenwich Street, Apt 927
New York, NY 10014
(212) 243-0652
WWW.JINSEY.COM

C. Day Photography
West 86th Street
(212) 873-5945

Dentato Studio
160 West 73rd Street
New York, NY 10023
(212) 595-7457

Socrates Diamant Photography
325 W 42nd Street #5A
New York, NY 10036
(212) 581-5859

John DiGennaro
16 Commerce Street
New York, NY 10014
(212) 675-2574

Benjamin Dimmitt
34 West 88th Street
New York, NY 10024
(212) 595-1816

Karol DuClos Photography
(212) 447-1993
www.karolduclos.com

Fahey-Bell Photography
47 East 3rd Street
New York, NY 10003
(212) 802-8003   (212) 473-1209

Daniel Falgerho
817 West End Avenue, #10C
New York, NY 10025
(212) 678-2068

Jeff Fasano Photography
101 West 85th Street
New York, NY 10024
(212) 595-3795

Andrew Fingland
20 East 42nd Street, 4F
New York , NY 10017
(212) 983-8909

John Firman
434 East 75th Street
New York, NY 10021
(212) 794-2794

Robert Fishman
111 West 19th Street
New York, NY 10011
(212) 206-0203

Fotofaces/William Newman
873 Broadway - Suite 605
New York, NY 10003
(212) 254-0669

Ira Fox Photography
(212) 606-4090

Kevin Fox
64 Thompson Street, #18
New York, NY 10012
(212) 925-4931
members.aol.com/foxfoto/site/

Joe Gaffney
334 West 77th Street
New York, NY 10024
(212) 787-0691 Fax: (212) 787-0929

David Garvey Photography
726 Tenth Avenue
New York, NY 10019
(212) 246-3230

Adam Gaynor Photography
277 West 10th Street, #1K
New York, NY 10011
(212) 691-2056

Jeff George Photographic
24 West 39th Street, 3rd Floor
New York, NY 10018
(212) 354-4933

Peter J. Gorman
Upper West Side Studio
(212) 580-7769

Nick Granito
35 East 28th Street
New York, NY 10016
(212) 684-1056

Debra Greenfield
142 East 16th Street
New York, NY 10003
(212) 533-0744 Fax: (212) 533-1562
dgreenfield@juno.com

Garry Gross
The Famous and Not So Famous Studio
(212) 807-7141

Rick Guidotti
43 East 20th Street
New York, NY 10003
(212) 420-1931
rickgnyc@aol.com

Manning Gurney
25 West 38th Street
New York, NY 10018
(212) 391-0965

Melissa Hamburg Photography
406 Central Park West
New York, NY 10025
(212) 662-6068

Michelle Hannay/Photographer of Women
250 East 73rd Street
New York, NY 10021
(212) 535-5466

John Hart
72nd Street and Riverside Drive
(212) 873-6585 Fax: (212) 688-7663

Brian Haviland Photography
34 East 30th Street, 4th Floor
New York, NY 10016
(212) 481-4132

Helen's Studio, a.k.a. Helen Miljakovich
144 Seventh Avenue, #3C
New York, NY 100011
(212) 242-0646

Harry Heleotis
25 Fifth Avenue
New York, NY 10003
(212) 260-1216

Joe Henson Photography
236 West 27th Street, Suite 10RW
New York, NY 10001
(212) 463-0575   Fax:(212) 463-0608

David Herrenbruck
(212) 494-5049

John Herrold
925 West End Avenue
New York, NY 10025
(212) 222-0040

Hoebermann Studio
281 Sixth Avenue at Bleecker Street
New York, NY 10014
(212) 807-8014

Jeffrey Hornstein Photography
137 West 14th Street, #301
New York, NY 10011
Tel/Fax: (212) 352-1186
Service: (212) 502-3463

Hot Shots Studios
(212) 563-4764
1-888-HEAD-SHOT

Dan Howell
216 West 18th Street
New York, NY 10011
(212) 242-3221
danhowl@mail.idt.net

David Hughes Photography
82 Irving Place, Apt#3E
New York, NY 10003
(212) 505-8576

Brooke Hunyady
(212) 505-9177

Michael Ian Studio
214 West 30th Street, 11th Floor
New York, NY 10001
(212) 947-0583

Eric Stephen Jacobs Studio
888 Eighth Avenue
New York, NY 10019
(212) 265-5566 Fax:(212) 265-5574
ericjacob@aol.com

Susan Johann
594 Broadway
New York, NY 10012
(212) 941-4151 Fax: (212) 274-1793

Ariel Jones Studio
11 Maiden Lane
New York, NY 10038
(212) 513-1090
arieljo@worldnet.att.net

the jussen studio
4 West 37th Street
New York, NY 10018
(212) 268-1340 Fax: (212) 695-1298
JUSPIX@aol.com

Sean Kahlil Studio
57 West 16th Street, 3rd Floor
New York, NY 10011
(212) 691-0213

Steve Kahn Photography
121 Mercer Street
New York, NY 10012
(212) 334-2139

Michael A. Kanakis
144 West 27th Street
New York, NY 10001
(212) 807-8232
Fax: (212) 414-4081
mkanakis@erols.com

Michael Keel Studio
42 Greene Street, 5th Floor
New York, NY 10013
(212) 274-0133
keelphoto@aol.com

Beth Kelly Photography
265 West 30th Street
New York, NY 10001
(212) 868-1604

KGM Studios
(212) 543-3782
(212) 769-6373

Michael Killoile Photography
219 East 10th Street
New York, NY 10003
(212) 228-8094

Robert Kim Photography
NY/LA: (888) 546-3686
www.robertkim.com

Alan Kirschen Photography
320 West 56th Street, #3E
New York, NY 10019
Tel/Fax: (212) 262-9504

Lorin Klaris
76 Ludlow Road
Westport, CT 06880
(212) 366-0635
(203) 227-9683

Steve Korn
211 East 70th Street, Suite 28C
New York, NY 10021
(212) 249-0995
stevephoto@prodigy.net

Karen Krause Photography
8 Beach Street, 4th Floor
New York, NY 10013
Tel/Fax: (212) 431-4046
kkphoto@juno.com

James J. Jr. Kriegsmann
939 Eighth Avenue
New York, NY 10019
(212) 247-0553 Fax: (212) 957-4281

Thomas O. Kriegsmann
208 West 29th Street, Rm 406
New York, NY 10001
(212) 279-1717

Krystyna Photography
453 East 14th Street, #12E
New York, NY 10009
(212) 673-5430

115

Timothy Lampson Photography
(212) 580-4438

Valeri Lantz
358 Broadway
New York, NY 10013
(212) 252-4528

Grant Leduc Photography
259 West 30th Street
New York, NY 10001
(212) 736-6221 Fax: (212) 736-0084

Elizabeth Lehmann Photography
(212) 362-5046

Ralph Lewin
156 West 74th Street
New York, NY 10023
(212) 580-0482

Lindholm Studio
131 Christie Street
New York, NY 10002
(212) 274-0466

Deborah Lopez
320 West 37th Street, #10A
New York, NY 10018
Tel/Fax: (212) 594-8273

Michael Louis
373 Broadway, Studio F3
New York, NY 10013
(212) 334-3507

Blanche Mackey
526 West 26th Street, #909
New York, NY 10001
(212) 633-6869

Robert Mannis
(212) 591-1285

Tania Mara Photography
201 West 74th Street, Studio 11G
New York, NY 10023
(212) 496-7248

Russell Maynor Studio
(212) 769-9728

RaNae Merrill Photography
26 West 96th Street, Suite 5R
New York, NY 10025
(212) 663-2719
www.rmerrillphoto.com

Chia Messina Photography
15 West 24th Street
New York, NY 10010
(212) 929-0917

Milca VDS
(212) 802-7567

Jonnie Miles
309 West 99th Street
New York, NY 10025
(212) 865-7956

David Morgan
39 West 14th Street, Suite 407
New York, NY 10011
(212) 989-3880

Bill Morris Studio
42 Greene Street
New York, NY 10013
(212) 274-1177
billm@billmorris.com

Stephen Mosher
448 West 49th Street, #2A
New York, NY 10019
(212) 245-6237

Catherine Nance
429 West 45th Street
New York, NY 10036
(212) 581-3915

Fernando Natalici
32 Union Square East, Suite 200
New York, NY 10003
(212) 473-0861 Fax: (212) 982-1550

Bob Newey
206 East 26th Street, 6th Floor
New York, NY 10010
(212) 532-4643

Dianora Niccolini
356 East 78th Street - By Appointment Only
New York, NY 10021
(212) 288-1698

Seon Park Photography
Phone: (917) 407-1491
Pager: (917) 303-6491

O'Brien Pictures
135 West 20th Street, 6th Floor
New York, NY 10011
(212) 366-1828 Fax: (212) 929-3450

Paul Olivier
481 Eighth Avenue
New York, NY 10001
(212) 947-1077

Mickey Pantano
(212) 505-2042

Paper Muse / Wayne Takenaka
44 West 37th Street
New York, NY 10018
(212) 564-5182

Eduardo Patino Photography
(212) 989-7808
(212) 245-0531

Nancy Pindrus Photography
21 West 68th Street
New York, NY 10023
(212) 799-8167

Christian Pollard
66-68 West 38th Street
New York, NY 10018
(212) 768-3990

Anthony Ragland Photography
66-68 West 38th Street, Suite 406
New York, NY 10018
(212) 582-1675
Service: (212) 724-2800

David Rapoport Computer Art,
Photography & Retouching
(212) 691-5528
davidr@interport.net   www.rapoport.com

Willis Roberts
238 West 56th Street, #12
New York, NY 10019
(212) 582-3832

Charles D. Robison
21 Stuyvesant Oval, Suite 3A
New York, NY 10009
(212) 777-4894

David Rodgers Photography
430 West 14th Street, Suite 207
New York, NY 10014
(212) 206-0180

Andrew Rosenthal Photography
448 West 37th Street, 6F
New York, NY 10018
(212) 760-0266

Mark Rubin
(212) 929-0293
mrubin@dorsai.org

Marie Ruggiero Photography and Retouching
185 East 85th Street
New York, NY 10028
(212) 534-3071

Gaetano Salvadore Photography
325 West 37th Street, 3rd Floor
New York, NY 10018
(212) 643-0270

John Sann Photography
394 Broadway, 6th Floor
New York, NY 10013
(212) 965-1210

Tim Schultheis Photography
155 West 73rd Street
New York, NY 10023
(212) 721-0829

Sebazco Photography
321 West 24th Street
New York, NY 10011
(212) 989-9170

Sevelo
50 West 34th Street, #23C5
New York, NY 10001
(212) 279-6911 Fax: (212) 643-5690

Diane Fay Skomars Photography
850 7th Avenue, #700
New York, NY 10019
(212) 459-3403

David Smith
Studio on 26th Street
(212) 647-8945

Speliotis Photography
13-17 Laight Street, F-2 #7
New York, NY 10013
(212) 966-0500

Philip Stark Photography
231 West 29th Street
New York, NY 10001
(212) 868-5555   Fax: (212) 868-5556

Tess Steinkolk / Brown Dog Productions
180 Varick Street, 12th Floor
New York, NY 10014
(212) 627-1366

David L. Stevens Photography
By Appointment Only
(212) 243-3635
DAV1014@aol.com

Laura Stiles Photography
(212) 998-6827

Deborah Stotzky
(212) 620-7720

Marion Suro
433 East 51st Street
New York, NY 10022
(212) 486-1630 Fax: (212) 486-4157

Gary Suson / Photofolio
397 West 12th Street
New York, NY 10014
(212) 802-7197

Peter Sweyer Photography
601 West 26th Street, 14th Floor
New York, NY10001
Studio Cell: (917) 488-7946

Lorraine Sylvestre Photography
119 West 23rd Street, Suite 206
New York, NY 10011
(212) 675-8134 Fax: (212) 242-0137

Nigel Teare Photography
38 West 26th Street, #10B
New York, NY 10010
(212) 243-3015

Thomson Photos
59 West 12th Street
New York, NY 10011
(212) 645-5540

Bob Van Lindt /van lindt CLASSICS
718-899-4610

Jim Varriale Inc.
26 West 74th Street
New York, NY 10023
(212) 874-2018

Barbara Vaughn Photography
111 4th Avenue
New York, NY 10003
(212) 529-0431

V. Max Photography
(212) 886-3720

Thaddeus Watkins Photography
252 West 37th Street, 18th Floor
New York, NY 10018
(212) 736-0776

Howard Wechsler
(212) 995-5219

Ken Weingart
304 East 20th Street, #2G
New York, NY 10003
(212) 979-8978

Denise Winters Photography
NY:(212) 355-5223
www.denisewinters.com

Scott Wynn Photography
(212) 874-1449

Sandy Zane
Greenwich Village
(212) 675-3331

New York State

Visage Studio Inc.
15 South Grand Avenue
Baldwin, NY 11510
(516) 724-4284

Outside New York

Elisabeth Burchard / Expressions Photography
253 Closterdock Road, Suite 6
Closter, NJ 07624
(201) 784-0210

Reginald Cheston Photography
2210 Long Brook Drive
Greensboro, NC 27406

Cathy Dixson Photography
358 W. Freemason Street, 1st Floor
Norfolk, VA 23510
(757) 625-2040 Fax: (757) 625-2225
cathyd@pilot.infi.net

Matthew Erulkar
2530 Chestnut Avenue
Ardmore, PA 19003
(610) 642-7760 Fax: (610) 642-9175

Christine Findlay PhotoGraphicArts
712 Sycamore Avenue
Red Bank, NJ 07701-4920
Voice: (732) 450-1010
Fax (732) 450-1060

DEJA VIEW Inc. / Larry Kosson
P.O.Box 43158
Upper Montclair, NJ 07043
(973) 746-6943

Paul Greco Photography
800 West Avenue, Suite C1
Miami Beach, FL 33139
(305) 672-4467

Peter Kind Studios
1533 South Broad Street
Philadelphia, PA 19147
(215) 336-2828
pk1734@aol.com

Bob Lasky Photography
1543 N.E. 123rd Street
North Miami, FL 33161
(305) 891-0550

Pam Manning / Manning Studio
1246 Westover Avenue, Suite #4
Norfolk, VA 23507
(757) 623-1871

Tony Mauer
432 24th Street
Virginia Beach, VA 23451
(757) 422-4469

Art Murphy
120 North Third Street
Philadelphia, PA 19106
(215) 928-0737

Deanna Neredith
73 Drennen Road
Orlando, FL 32806
(407) 851-6130
dphoto31@aol.com

Lynn Parks Photography
1700 S.Bayshore Lane, Studio 6A
Coconut Grove, FL 33133
(305) 673-0170 Fax: (305) 673-0046
lens@lynnparks.com

Ron Rinaldi Digital Photography
1518 Courtney Avenue
Hollywood, CA 90046
(323) 874-5269

Danny Sanchez Photographer
8-10 Broad Street
Red Bank, NJ 07701
(908) 530-4120 Fax: (908) 530-0146

Scott Singer Photography
261 N.E. 32nd Court
Ft. Lauderdale, FL 33334
(954) 563-1787   Voice Mail: (954) 360-3111

J.R. Sterling Photography
6810 Silver Star Road
Orlando, FL 32818
(407) 297-9222

Charles Swift / Creative Focus
412 Cold Spring Road
Virginia Beach, VA 23454-4011
(757) 340-0797

Bob & Pamela Weidner / Stagelight
Photography
5101 Hunters Trail
Wilmington, NC 28405
(910) 792-1720 Fax: (910) 397-0877

ILFORD
BLACK & WHITE
PRODUCTS

212-463-0575

© Joe Henson 1999

119

*For more information...

about any photographer, advertiser or laboratory service offered in this book, circle corresponding number found in contents and further details will be provided. All advertisers wish to thank you for your inquiries.

Reproductions

READER RESPONSE CARD

See Table Of Contents for Reader Response numbers

Please send information circled -
(See Table Of Contents for Photographers' Response number).

6	8	10	12	13	14	16	17	18
20	22	24	26	28	30	32	33	34
36	38	40	42	44	46	48	50	52
54	56	58	60	62	64	65	66	67
68	70	71	72	74	76	78	80	81
82	84	86	88	90	91	92	94	95
96	97	98	100	102	103	104	106	107
108	109	110	120					

Name (please print)

Address   Phone (optional)

City   State   Zip

Reproductions

READER RESPONSE CARD

See Table Of Contents for Reader Response numbers

Please send information circled -
(See Table Of Contents for Photographers' Response number).

6	8	10	12	13	14	16	17	18
20	22	24	26	28	30	32	33	34
36	38	40	42	44	46	48	50	52
54	56	58	60	62	64	65	66	67
68	70	71	72	74	76	78	80	81
82	84	86	88	90	91	92	94	95
96	97	98	100	102	103	104	106	107
108	109	110	120					

Name (please print)

Address   Phone (optional)

City   State   Zip

Reproductions

6 West 37th St., 4th Floor
New York, NY 10018

Reproductions

6 West 37th St., 4th Floor
New York, NY 10018